E.M.I. MUSIC PUBLISHING LIMITED/MUSIC SALES LIMITED.

BOOK DESIGN BY
PEARCE MARCHBANK

DISTRIBUTED BY:
MUSIC SALES LIMITED, 78 NEWMAN STREET, LONDON W1P 3LA
E.M.I. MUSIC PUBLISHING LIMITED, 138-140 CHARING CROSS ROAD, LONDON WC2H 0LD.

ISBN 0.86001-650.1
ORDER NO. AM 24498

PRINTED IN GREAT BRITAIN BY
LOWE & BRYDONE PRINTERS LIMITED, THETFORD, NORFOLK

BEST OF THE ROLLING STONES

VOLUME TWO 1972-1978

MISS YOU

WORDS AND MUSIC BY MICK JAGGER AND KEITH RICHARD

I've been hold-ing out so long,___ I've been sleep-ing all a-lone,___ Lord I

miss you,___ I've been hang-ing on the phone, I've been

(spoken) I've been

walk - ing Cen - tral Park, __ sing - ing af - ter dark, __ Peo - ple think I'm __ cra -

- zy, I've been stum - bling on my feet __ shuf - fling thro' the street __ ask - ing

peo - ple, "What's the mat - ter with you Jim boy?" Some - times

ALL DOWN THE LINE

WORDS AND MUSIC BY MICK JAGGER AND KEITH RICHARD

FINGERPRINT FILE

WORDS AND MUSIC BY MICK JAGGER AND KEITH RICHARD

Cm7

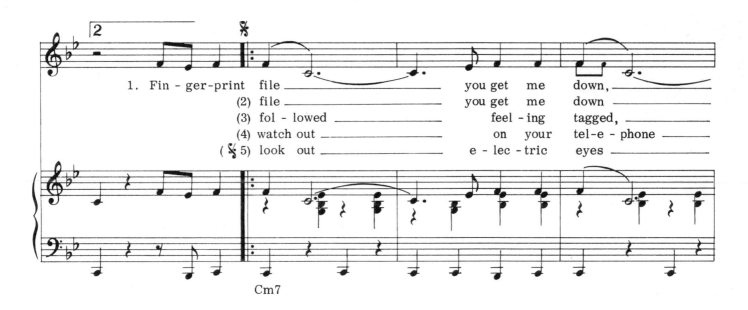

1. Fin - ger-print file _____ you get me down, _____
(2) file _____ you get me down _____
(3) fol - lowed _____ feel - ing tagged, _____
(4) watch out _____ on your tel-e-phone _____
(5) look out _____ e - lec -tric eyes _____

Cm7

_____ you get me run - ning _____ know my way a - round _____
_____ you get me run - ning _____ keep me on the ground _____
_____ cross-ing wat - er _____ try - ing to wipe my tracks _____
_____ wrong num - ber _____ they know you ain't home _____
_____ rats on the sell out _____ who gon - na tes - ti - fy _____

F7

Spoken "Hallo baby

Mm - mm

Ah, yeah you know we ain't talkin' alone

Who's listening

But I don't really know

But you better tell the sis to keep out of sight

'Cause I know they takin' pictures on the ultraviolet light

Yes

Aah but these days it's all secrecy not privacy

Shoot first, that's right, ... you know

Bye bye

Who's listening

Right now, somebody is listening to you

Keeping their eyes peeled on you

Mmmh mmmh what a price, what a price to pay

All right

Good night, sleep tight".

IT'S ONLY ROCK 'N' ROLL

WORDS AND MUSIC BY MICK JAGGER AND KEITH RICHARD

RESPECTABLE

WORDS AND MUSIC BY MICK JAGGER AND KEITH RICHARD

Medium Rock

Well now we're res-pec-ted in so - ci - e -ty,___ you ain't wor-
now you're a pil-lar of so - ci - e -ty,___you're not wor-

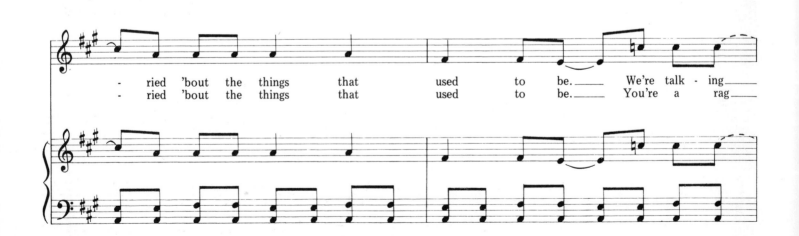

-ried 'bout the things that used to be.___ We're talk - ing___
-ried 'bout the things that used to be.___ You're a rag___

FARAWAY EYES

WORDS AND MUSIC BY MICK JAGGER AND KEITH RICHARD

1. I _ _ was _ _ _ driving _ _ _ home, _ _ _ early _ _ _ Sunday _ _ _ morning _ _ _ through _ _ _
2. I _ _ had _ an _ arrangement _ to _ _ meet _ a _ girl, _ _ and _ I _ was _ kind _ of _ late, _ _ And _ _
3. Well _ the _ _ preacher _ _ kept _ _ right _ on _ _ saying _ _ that _ all _ I _ had _ to _ _ do _ was _ _

DOO DOO DOO DOO DOO
HEARTBREAKER

WORDS AND MUSIC BY MICK JAGGER AND KEITH RICHARD

The po-lice in New York ci-ty___ chased a boy right through the park___

And in a case of mis-ta-ken I-den-ti-ty___ they put a bul-let through his heart___

Heart break-er___ with your for-ty four___ I wan-na tear your world a-part___

Heart break - er__ with your for - ty - four
I wan - na tear your world a - part__

A ten_ year old girl on a street cor - ner
stick - ing need - les in her arm__ She died__

____ in the dirt of the al - ley way__
her mo - ther said she had__ no chance no chance

Heart break - er heart break - er she stuck the pins right in her heart__
you stole the love right out of my heart__

BEFORE THEY MAKE ME RUN

WORDS AND MUSIC BY MICK JAGGER AND KEITH RICHARD

Worked the bars and side_____ shows,____ a
Watch my tail-lights fad - - ing, there ain't a

- long the twi - light zone,____ On - ly a crowd____ can make you
dry eye in the house,____ They're laugh - in' and sing - in'; well they're

BEAST OF BURDEN

WORDS AND MUSIC BY MICK JAGGER AND KEITH RICHARD

not too blind ___ to see, _____ Oh lit - tle sis - ter__

_ pret - ty, pret - ty, pret - ty, pret - ty girl, ___

You're a

FOOL TO CRY
WORDS AND MUSIC BY MICK JAGGER AND KEITH RICHARD

When I come home, ba-by,
I got a wom-an,

and I've been work-ing all night long,____
and she live in a poor part of town,

I put my daugh-ter on my
and I go see her some -

C   Dm

"Oo,   Dad - dy, you're a   fool   to   cry,   you're a

B♭maj7   G9   A7

fool   to   cry,   and   it   makes   me   won - der   why.

Repeat ad lib

Dm   G9   A7   Dm

(vocal ad lib)

Repeat ad lib

Vocal Ad Lib

I'm a fool, baby,
I'm a fool, baby,
I'm a certified fool, now
I want to tell ya,
Gotta tell ya, baby,
I'm a fool, baby,
Certified fool for ya, mama, come on,
I'm a fool, I'm a fool,
I'm a fool.

HAPPY

WORDS AND MUSIC BY MICK JAGGER AND KEITH RICHARD

SWEET VIRGINIA

WORDS AND MUSIC BY MICK JAGGER AND KEITH RICHARD

DANCING WITH MR. D

WORDS AND MUSIC BY MICK JAGGER AND KEITH RICHARD

1. Down in the grave - yard where we have our tryst the air smells sweet the air smells thick He nev - er smiles his mouth mere - ly twists The breath in my lungs feels cling - ing and thick Now

2. Will it be poison in my glass
   Will it be slow or will it be fast
   The bite of a snake the sting of a spider
   A drink of belladonna of a Toussaint night
   Hiding round a corner in New York city
   Looking down a 44 in West Virginia
   I was dancing, dancing, dancing so free
   I was dancing, dancing, dancing so free
   Dancing with Mister D.

   Mister D. Mister D. Mister D. Mister D.
   Dancing, dancing, dancing, dancing
   Dancing, dancing, dancing, dancing

   Dancing, dancing dancing so free
   I was dancing, dancing, dancing so free
   Dancing Lord take your hands off me
   Dancing with Mister D. Mister D. Mister D.

3. One night I was dancing with a lady in black
   Wearing black silk gloves and a black silk hat
   She looked at me longing with black velvet eyes
   She gazed at me strange all cunning and wise
   Then I saw the flesh just fall off her bones
   The eyes in her skull were just burning like coals
   Lord have mercy fire and brimstone
   I was dancing with Mister D.
   Dancing, dancing, dancing so free
   I was dancing, dancing, dancing so free
   Dancing Lord take your hands off me
   Dancing with Mister D.

SHINE A LIGHT

WORDS AND MUSIC BY MICK JAGGER AND KEITH RICHARD

Slowly, with a beat

Saw you stretched out___ in Room Ten-O-Nine with a smile___ on your face___ and a

tear right in your eye.___ Could-n't see___ to get a line on you, my sweet___hon -ey love.

Ber-ber jew -'lry___ jan - gling___ down___ the street,___

make you shut your eyes___ at ev -'ry wom-an that you meet. Could not seem___ to get a

TURD ON THE RUN

WORDS AND MUSIC BY MICK JAGGER AND KEITH RICHARD

Grabbed hold of your coat - tail but it come off in my hand,_____ I
reached for your la-pel_____ but it weren't sewn on so grand.___
Begged, prom-ised an - y - thing_ if on - ly you would stay,___ well, I

boo-gied in_ the dark;_____ Tie your hands,_ tie your feet,_

throw you to the sharks._ Make you sweat,_ make you scream,_

make you wish_ you'd nev-er been,_ I lost a lot of love__ o-ver you,_

Repeat and fade

Repeat and fade

ROCKS OFF

WORDS AND MUSIC BY MICK JAGGER AND KEITH RICHARD

SOME GIRLS

WORDS AND MUSIC BY MICK JAGGER AND KEITH RICHARD

Slow Rock Beat

1. Some girls give me mon - ey,_____
5. French girls they want Car - ti - er,_____ I

some girls give me clothes;_____ some girls give me jewel - 'ry_____ that I'd
- ta - li - an girls want cars;_____ A - me - ri - can girls want ev - 'ry - thing in the world you could

ne - ver thought___ I'd own.
pos - si - bly___ i - ma - gine.

2. Some girls give me dia - monds,___
6. En - glish girls they're so pris - sy___ I can't

some girls heart at - tacks;___
stand them on the te - le - phone;___

some girls I give all my bread to
some - times I take the re - cei - ver off the hook, I don't want

I don't e - ver want it back.___
them to e - ver call at home.___

3. Some girls give me jewel - 'ry,___
7. White girls they're pret - ty fun - ny,___

oth - ers   buy me clothes;___   some   girls give me child - ren_____   I
some-times they drive me mad; ___   black girls just want to get fucked all night__ I just don't

ne - ver ask for.   *(Instr.)* _____
have that much jam.   8. Chi - nese girls__ they're so gen - tle, _____ they're

real - ly such__ a tease;   you ne - ver know quite what they're cook-ing_____   in

Sing both times

- side those sil - ky sleeves. }   Give me all _____ your mon - ey, _____

HOT STUFF

WORDS AND MUSIC BY MICK JAGGER AND KEITH RICHARD

2. Everybody on the dance floor,
   You know what I'm talking about.
   Music make you forget all your troubles,
   Make you sing and make it tell the whole wide world.
   So what, hot stuff, shake it up.

3. I want to tell all my friends in London
   There ain't nothing wrong with you,
   But you'd better shape up.
   Shake it up, you're hot stuff.

4. All the people in New York City
   I know you're going broke,
   But I know you're tough.
   Yeah, you're hot stuff, hot stuff.

5. To everybody in Jamaica that's working in the sun,
   You're hot, you're hot, you're hot stuff.
   Shake it up, shake it up,
   Hot stuff, hot stuff.

MEMORY MOTEL

WORDS AND MUSIC BY MICK JAGGER AND KEITH RICHARD

Moderately slow

1. Han-nah hon-ey was a peach-y kind of girl; her eyes were ha-zel and her nose was slight-ly curved.

1.2. She got a mind ___ of her own, ___ yeah, _ and she use it might-y fine. ___

2. She drove a pick-up truck painted green and blue;
   The tires were wearing thin, she done a mile or two.
   And when I asked her where she headed for,
   "Back up to Boston, I'm singing in a bar."
   I got to fly today on down to Baton Rouge;
   My nerves are shot already, the road ain't all that smooth.
   Across in Texas is the rose of San Antone;
   I keep on a-feeling that gnawing in my bones.

            (Chorus)

3. On the seventh day my eyes were all aglaze;
   We been ten thousand miles and been in fifteen states.
   Every woman seemed to fade out of my mind;
   I hit the bottle and I hit the sack and cried.
   What's all this laughter on the twenty-second floor?
   It's just some friends of mine and they're busting down the doors.
   It's been a lonely night at the Memory Motel.

            (Chorus)

SOUL SURVIVOR

WORDS AND MUSIC BY MICK JAGGER AND KEITH RICHARD

Moderate Rock

1. When the wa-ters is rough _____ the sail-ing is tough, _____ I'll get drowned in your love. _____

You've got a cut throat crew, _____ I'm gon-na

won't be,____ you're gon-na be the death of me.___

D.S. 𝄋 *and fade*